PUFFIN BOOKS

The poems in this anthology have been chosen for the simplicity and directness of approach which is so much part of a child's own vision. The idea running through it is man's part in the whole of creation, sharing the earth in equal partnership with all living things, even to the snake in the grass and the fly on the windowpane. The selection is fresh and unusual; most people will find in it something new to them, and surely every child will find pleasure and delight in its pages. The verses are gathered into small groups, with suggestive headings such as *Sharing the Earth, I Watched a Nest, Wonderful Ways, Welcome and Unwelcome Beasts, Loving Kindness,* etc.

In an article on children and poetry in *Junior Bookshelf,* Leila Berg spoke of quality 'which reveals simple ordinary things seen suddenly with intensity, tenderness, and meaning'. This describes very well what guided her in her choice of material.

Four Feet and Two

AND SOME WITH NONE

AN ANTHOLOGY OF VERSE COMPILED BY

 Leila Berg

WITH ILLUSTRATIONS BY
SHIRLEY BURKE **AND** MARVIN BILECK

PENGUIN BOOKS

Penguin Books Ltd, Harmondsworth, Middlesex
U.S.A.: Penguin Books Inc., 3300 Clipper Mill Road, Baltimore 11, Md
AUSTRALIA: Penguin Books Pty Ltd, 762 Whitehorse Road,
Mitcham, Victoria

—

This selection first published in Puffin Books 1960

Made and printed in Great Britain
by Cox & Wyman Ltd, London,
Fakenham and Reading

Contents

6. WELCOME AND UNWELCOME BEASTS

9. SPECIAL MOMENTS

10. DIFFERENT LIVES

11. GLORY AND ETERNITY

Acknowledgements

We wish to thank Padraic Colum, Gwen Dunn, Eleanor Farjeon, W. W. Gibson, Sir Alexander Gray, Eden Phillpotts, Anthony Rye, the Hon. V. Sackville-West, Francis Scarfe, E. Lucia Turnbull, and Margaret Stanley-Wrench for permission to reprint their poems in this anthology. Eleanor Farjeon's 'The Golden Cat', 'Mrs Peck Pigeon', and 'House Hunters' are reprinted from *Over the Garden Wall* by Eleanor Farjeon; Copyright 1933–1951 by Eleanor Farjeon; published by J. B. Lippincott Company. Francis Scarfe's 'Cats' is reprinted from *Underworlds* (Heinemann). We would also like to thank Mrs Helen Thomas for permission to include poems by Edward Thomas; the Society of Authors and Miss Pamela Hinkson for Katherine Tynan's 'Larks'; and Miss Ann Wolfe for 'The Blackbird' and 'The Grey Squirrel' by Humbert Wolfe. We also thank *The Countryman* for permission to quote poems by S. Thomas Ansell, John Buxton, Mary Holden, Betty Hughes, J. E. M., and Eleanor Glenn Wallis. Hilaire Belloc's 'Jack and his Pony, Tom' and 'The Frog' are reprinted from *Cautionary Verses* by Hilaire Belloc, by permission of Alfred A. Knopf Inc. (Copyright 1931 by Hilaire Belloc) and Gerald Duckworth & Co Ltd. Edmund Blunden's 'The Barn' is reprinted from *The Waggoner* by Edmund Blunden, by permission of Sidgwick & Jackson Ltd. Elizabeth Coatsworth's 'No Shop Does the Bird Use' and 'Now is the Time' are reprinted from *Poems* by Elizabeth Coatsworth (© 1934, 1937, 1939, 1940, 1942, 1946, 1948, 1950, 1951, 1957 by The Macmillan Company), and 'On a Night of Snow' from *Night and the Cat* by Elizabeth Coatsworth, by permission of The Macmillan Company, New York. Frances Cornford's 'Night Song' and 'A Child's Dream' are reprinted by permission of Mrs Cornford and the Cresset Press. W. H. Davies's 'Jenny Wren' and 'A Great Time' are reprinted from *The Collected Poems of W. H. Davies* by permission of Mrs H. M. Davies and Jonathan Cape Ltd. Walter de la Mare's poems are reprinted by permission of the Literary Trustees of Walter de la Mare and the Society of Authors as their representative, John Drinkwater's 'Blackbird' is reprinted by permission of Sidgwick & Jackson Ltd. The extract from Clifford Dyment's 'Hedgehog in an Air Raid' is reprinted from *Axe in the Wood* by permission of J. M. Dent & Sons Ltd. T. S. Eliot's 'The Rum Tum Tugger' is reprinted from *Old Possum's Book of Practical Cats* by permission of Faber & Faber Ltd and Harcourt, Brace & Company Inc. Robert Frost's 'The Pasture', 'The Runaway', 'Dust of Snow', 'Come In', and 'Fireflies in the Garden' are reprinted from *You Come*

Sharing the Earth

One Family

ISAIAH

The wolf also shall dwell with the lamb,
And the leopard shall lie down with the kid;
And the calf and the young lion and the fatling together;
And a little child shall lead them.
And the cow and the bear shall feed;
Their young ones shall lie down together;
And the lion shall eat straw like the ox.
And the sucking child shall play on the hole of the asp,
And the weaned child shall put his hand on the cocka-
trice's den.
They shall not hurt nor destroy
In all my holy mountain:
For the earth shall be full of the knowledge of the Lord,
As the waters cover the sea.

City Mouse and Garden Mouse

CHRISTINA ROSSETTI

The city mouse lives in a house,
The garden mouse lives in a bower;
He's friendly with the frogs and toads,
And sees the pretty plants in flower.

The city mouse eats bread and cheese,
The garden mouse eats what he can;
We will not grudge him seeds and stocks,
Poor little timid, furry man.

The Rabbit

ELIZABETH MADOX ROBERTS

When they said the time to hide was mine,
I hid back under a thick grape vine.

And while I was still for the time to pass,
A little grey thing came out of the grass.

He hopped his way through the melon bed
And sat down close by a cabbage head.

He sat down close where I could see,
And his big still eyes looked hard at me,

His big eyes bursting out of the rim,
And I looked back very hard at him.

To a Fish of the Brook

JOHN WOLCOT

Why flyest thou away with fear?
Trust me, there's naught of danger near,
    I have no wicked hook
All covered with a snaring bait,
Alas, to tempt thee to thy fate,
    And drag thee from the brook.

O harmless tenant of the flood,
I do not wish to spill thy blood,
    For nature unto thee
Perchance hath given a tender wife,
And children dear, to charm thy life,
    As she hath done for me.

Enjoy thy stream, O harmless fish;
And when an angler for his dish,
    Through gluttony's vile sin
Attempts, a wretch, to pull thee *out*,
God give thee strength, O gentle trout,
    To pull the rascal *in*!

Meeting

CLIFFORD DYMENT

Over the grass a hedgehog came
Questing the air for scents of food
And the cracked twig of danger.
He shuffled near in the gloom. Then stopped.
He was aware of me. I went up,
Bent low to look at him, and saw
His coat of lances pointing to my hand.
What could I do
To show I was no enemy?
I turned him over, inspected his small clenched paws,
His eyes expressionless as glass,
And did not know how I could speak,
By tongue or touch, the language of a friend.

It was a grief to be a friend
Yet to be dumb; to offer peace
And bring the soldiers out . . .

(from *Hedgehog in an Air Raid*)

The Grey Squirrel

HUMBERT WOLFE

Like a small grey
coffee-pot,
sits the squirrel.
He is not

all he should be,
kills by dozens
trees, and eats
his red-brown cousins.

The keeper on the
other hand,
who shot him, is
a Christian, and

loves his enemies,
which shows
the squirrel was not
one of those.

Enjoyment

THOMAS HOOD

Play on, ye timid Rabbits!
For I can see ye run,
Ne'er thinking of a gun,
Or of the ferret's habits.

Ye sportive Hares! go forcing
The dewdrop from the bent;
My mind is not intent
On greyhounds or on coursing.

Feed on, ye gorgeous Pheasants!
My sight I do not vex
With cords about your necks
Forestalling you for presents.

Go gazing on, and bounding,
Thou solitary Deer!
My fancy does not hear
Hounds braying, and horns sounding.

Each furr'd or feather'd creature,
Enjoy with me this earth,
Its life, its love, its mirth,
And die the death of nature.

Winter Rain

CHRISTINA ROSSETTI

Every valley drinks,
    Every dell and hollow;
Where the kind rain sinks and sinks,
    Green of Spring will follow.

Yet a lapse of weeks –
    Buds will burst their edges,
Strip their wool-coats, glue-coats, streaks,
    In the woods and hedges;

Weave a bower of love
    For birds to meet each other,
Weave a canopy above
    Nest and egg and mother.

But for fattening rain
    We should have no flowers,
Never a bud or leaf again
    But for soaking showers;

Never a mated bird
    In the rocking tree-tops,
Never indeed a flock or herd
    To graze upon the lea-crops.

Lambs so woolly white,
　　Sheep the sun-bright leas on,
They could have no grass to bite
　　But for rain in season.

We should find no moss
　　In the shadiest places,
Find no waving meadow grass
　　Pied with broad-eyed daisies:

But miles of barred sand,
　　With never a son or daughter;
Not a lily on the land,
　　Or lily on the water.

Flocks and Herds

A Saxon Song

V. SACKVILLE-WEST

Leisurely flocks and herds,
Cool-eyed cattle that come
Mildly to wonted words,
Swine that in orchards roam –
A man and his beasts make a man and his home.

Milking Song

CHRISTINA ROSSETTI

Brownie, Brownie, let down your milk,
White as swansdown and smooth as silk,
Fresh as dew and pure as snow:
For I know where the cowslips blow,
And you shall have a cowslip wreath
No sweeter scented than your breath.

The Pasture

ROBERT FROST

I'm going out to clean the pasture spring;
I'll only stop to rake the leaves away
(And wait to watch the water clear, I may);
I shan't be gone long. – You come too.

I'm going out to fetch the little calf
That's standing by the mother. It's so young
It totters when she licks it with her tongue.
I shan't be gone long. – You come too.

'Thank you, Pretty Cow'

JANE *and* ANN TAYLOR

Thank you, pretty cow, that made
Pleasant milk to soak my bread,
Every day and every night,
Warm, and fresh, and sweet, and white.

Do not chew the hemlock rank,
Growing on the weedy bank;
But the yellow cowslips eat,
They will make it very sweet.

Where the purple violet grows,
Where the bubbling water flows,
Where the grass is fresh and fine,
Pretty cow, go there and dine.

Numbers

LOUIS GOLDING

Three sheep graze on the low hill
    Beneath the shadow of five trees,
        Three sheep !
    Five old sycamores !
(The noon is very full of sleep.
The noon's a shepherd kind and still.
The noon's a shepherd takes his ease
Beneath the shadow of five trees,
    Five old sycamores.)
Three sheep graze on the low hill.
Down in the grass in twos and fours
Cows are munching in the field.
Three sheep graze on the low hill;
Bless them, Lord, to give me wool.
Cows are munching in the field;
Bless them that their teats be full.
Bless the sheep and cows to yield
Wool to keep my children warm,
Milk that they should grow therefrom.

Shadows

WALTER DE LA MARE

The horse in the field,
The cows in the meadow,
Each browses and swishes
Plumb over its shadow –

It is noon. And beneath
That old thorn on the steep
A shepherd and sheepdog
Sit watching their sheep.

The Cow

R. L. STEVENSON

The friendly cow, all red and white,
I love with all my heart:
She gives me cream with all her might,
To eat with apple-tart.

She wanders lowing here and there,
And yet she cannot stray,
All in the pleasant open air,
The pleasant light of day;

And blown by all the winds that pass
And wet with all the showers,
She walks among the meadow grass
And eats the meadow flowers.

The Moo-Cow-Moo

EDMUND VANCE COOK

The moo-cow-moo has a tail like rope,
An' it's ravelled down where it grows,
An' it's jest like feelin' a piece of soap
All over the moo-cow's nose.

The moo-cow-moo has lots of fun
Jest swingin' its tail about,
But ef he opens his mouth, I run,
Cause that's where the moo comes out.

Spring Song

CHRISTINA ROSSETTI

On the grassy banks
Lambkins at their pranks;
Woolly sisters, woolly brothers
    Jumping off their feet
While their woolly mothers
    Watch by them and bleat.

The Lambs of Grasmere, 1860

CHRISTINA ROSSETTI

The upland flocks grew starved and thinned:
    Their shepherds scarce could feed the lambs
Whose milkless mothers butted them,
    Or who were orphaned of their dams.
The lambs athirst for mother's milk
    Filled all the place with piteous sounds:
Their mothers' bones made white for miles
    The pastureless wet pasture grounds.

Day after day, night after night,
    From lamb to lamb the shepherds went,
With teapots for the bleating mouths,
    Instead of nature's nourishment.
The little shivering gaping things
    Soon knew the step that brought them aid,
And fondled the protecting hand,
    And rubbed it with a woolly head.

Then, as the days waxed on to weeks,
    It was a pretty sight to see
These lambs with frisky heads and tails
    Skipping and leaping on the lea,
Bleating in tender, trustful tones,
    Resting on rocky crag or mound,
And following the beloved feet
    That once had sought for them and found.

These very shepherds of their flocks,
    These loving lambs so meek to please
Are worthy of recording words
    And honour in their due degrees:
So I might live a hundred years,
    And roam from strand to foreign strand,
Yet not forget this flooded spring
    And scarce-saved lambs of Westmoreland.

No Rain

JEREMIAH

Because the ground is chapt,
For there was no rain in the earth,
The ploughmen were ashamed,
They covered their heads.
Yea, the hind also calved in the field and forsook it,
Because there was no grass.
And the wild asses did stand in the high places,
They snuffed up the wind like dragons;
Their eyes did fail, because there was no grass.

I watched a Nest

The Nest

CHRISTINA ROSSETTI

I watched a nest from day to day,
    A green nest full of pleasant shade,
    Wherein three speckled eggs were laid:
But when they should have hatched in May,
    The two old birds had grown afraid
Or tired, and flew away.

(from *Symbols*)

Swallows over the South Downs

MARY HOLDEN

England, we're here again,
Sleet-squalls and blinding rain
(All just as usual)
    Greet us on landing.
Head-winds through Italy,
Fog over Brittany,
Why we don't give it up 's
    Past understanding.

Buffeted, blown, half-dead . . .
Hey, look, there's Beachy Head!
Green turf and milky-white
    Chalk-cliffs like Dover!
Sun-gleams at last, hurray!
. . . I'm off down Uckfield way,
Country'll be looking grand
    Now the rain's over.

. . . Primroses, blowing leaves,
Thatched roofs and cottage eaves,
Oast-houses, dusky-dark,
    What sites for nesting!
Come on, the fun's begun,
Hurry up, everyone,
Don't let's waste any time
    Preening and resting . . .

House Hunters

ELEANOR FARJEON

Birds will be house-hunting
Soon – think of that!
Crows in the elm-tops
And larks on the flat,
Owls in the belfry
And wren in the leaves,
And swifts will go house-hunting
Under the eaves.

Moorhen will hunt for her
House in the reeds,
Chaffinch the apple-tree
Bough ere she breeds,
Thrush in the hollow oak,
Sparrow won't care –
Here, there and everywhere,
Any old where!

Cuckoo won't trouble,
She'll just stop and call,
But starling and nightingale,
Blackbird and all,
Jays as they chatter,
And doves as they croon,
Soon will be house-hunting,
Think of it – soon!

Spring

E. LUCIA TURNBULL

'My dear,' said Mrs Wren, 'if Mrs Cuckoo comes to
    call,
I really think it would be best to see her in the hall,
Explaining that our house it is so very, very small
We have no room for paying guests, or any guests at all.'

The Thrush's Nest

JOHN CLARE

Within a thick and spreading hawthorn bush,
That overhung a molehill large and round,
I heard from morn to morn a merry thrush
Sing hymns to sunrise, and I drank the sound
With joy; and often, an intruding guest,
I watched her secret toil from day to day
How true she warped the moss, to form a nest,
And modelled it within with wood and clay;
And by-and-by, like heath bells gilt with dew,
There lay her shining eggs, as bright as flowers,
Ink-spotted over shells of greeny blue;
And there I witnessed in the sunny hours,
A brood of Nature's minstrels chirp and fly,
Glad as the sunshine and the laughing sky.

Rhyme

CHRISTINA ROSSETTI

Hear what the mournful linnets say:
    'We built our nest compact and warm,
But cruel boys came round our way
    And took our summerhouse by storm.

'They crushed the eggs so neatly laid;
    So now we sit with drooping wing,
And watch the ruin they have made,
    Too late to build, too sad to sing.'

Nest Eggs

ROBERT LOUIS STEVENSON

Birds all the sunny day
      Flutter and quarrel
Here in the arbour-like
      Tent of the laurel.

Here in the fork
      The brown nest is seated;
Four little blue eggs
      The mother keeps heated.

While we stand watching her,
      Staring like gabies,
Safe in each egg are the
      Bird's little babies.

Soon the frail eggs they shall
      Chip, and upspringing
Make all the April woods
      Merry with singing.

Younger than we are,
      O children, and frailer,
Soon in blue air they'll be
      Singer and sailor.

We, so much older,
    Taller and stronger,
We shall look down on the
    Birdies no longer.

They shall go flying
    With musical speeches
High overhead in the
    Tops of the beeches.

In spite of our wisdom
    And sensible talking,
We on our feet must go
    Plodding and walking.

Child's Talk in April

CHRISTINA ROSSETTI

I wish you were a pleasant wren,
    And I your small accepted mate;
How we'd look down on toilsome men!
    We'd rise and go to bed at eight
    Or it may be not quite so late.

Then you should see the nest I'd build,
    The wondrous nest for you and me;
The outside rough perhaps, but filled
    With wool and down; ah you should see
    The cosy nest that it would be.

We'd have our change of hope and fear,
    Small quarrels, reconcilements sweet:
I'd perch by you to chirp and cheer,
    Or hop about on active feet,
    And fetch you dainty bits to eat.

We'd be so happy by the day,
    So safe and happy through the night,
We both should feel, and I should say,
    It's all one season of delight,
And we'll make merry while we may.

Perhaps some day there'd be an egg
    When spring had blossomed from the snow:

I'd stand triumphant on one leg;
    Like chanticleer I'd almost crow
    To let our little neighbours know.

Next you should sit and I would sing
Through lengthening days of sunny spring;
    Till, if you wearied of the task,
I'd sit; and you should spread your wing
    From bough to bough; I'd sit and bask.

Fancy the breaking of the shell,
    The chirp, the chickens wet and bare,
The untried proud paternal swell;
    And you with housewife-matron air
    Enacting choicer bills of fare.

Fancy the embryo coats of down,
    The gradual feathers soft and sleek;
Till clothed and strong from tail to crown,
    With virgin warblings in their beak,
    They too go forth and seek.

So would it last an April through
And early summer fresh with dew –
    Then should we part and live as twain:
Love-time would bring me back to you,
    And build our happy nest again.

The Ostrich

JOB

The wing of the ostrich rejoiceth;
But are her pinions and feathers kindly?
For she leaveth her eggs on the earth,
And warmeth them in the dust,
And forgetteth that the foot may crush them,
Or that the wild beast may trample them.
She is hardened against her young ones, as if they were
    not hers:
Though her labour be in vain, she is without fear;
Because God hath deprived her of wisdom,
Neither hath he imparted to her understanding.

Bird Song

Any Bird

J.E.M.

The bird in the branches sings and sings
    And raindrops fall from the shaken spray,
The only song he knows he sings
    The only way.

The Blackbird

HUMBERT WOLFE

In the far corner,
Close by the swings,
Every morning
A blackbird sings.

His bill's so yellow,
His coat's so black,
That he makes a fellow
Whistle back.

Ann, my daughter,
Thinks that he
Sings for us two
Especially.

Speech

WALTER DE LA MARE

The robin's whistled stave
Is tart as half-ripened fruit;
Wood-sooth from bower of leaves
The blackbird's flute;
Shrill-small the ardent wren's;
And the thrush, and the long-tailed tit –
Each hath its own apt tongue,
     Shrill, harsh or sweet.

Blackbird

JOHN DRINKWATER

He comes on chosen evenings,
My blackbird bountiful, and sings
Over the gardens of the town
Just at the hour the sun goes down.
His flight across the chimneys thick,
By some divine arithmetic,
Comes to his customary stack,
And couches there his plumage black,
And there he lifts his yellow bill,
Kindled against the sunset, till
These suburbs are like Dymock woods
Where music has her solitudes,
And while he mocks the winter's wrong
Rapt on his pinnacle of song,
Figured above our garden plots,
Those are celestial chimney-pots.

To a Skylark

PERCY BYSSHE SHELLEY

Higher still and higher,
From the earth thou springest,
Like a cloud of fire,
The blue deep thou wingest,
And singing still dost soar, and soaring ever singest.

A Green Cornfield

CHRISTINA ROSSETTI

The earth was green, the sky was blue:
    I saw and heard one sunny morn
A skylark hang between the two,
    A singing speck above the corn;

A stage below, in gay accord,
    White butterflies danced on the wing,
And still the singing skylark soared,
    And silent sank and soared to sing.

The cornfield stretched a tender green
    To right and left beside my walks;
I knew he had a nest unseen
    Somewhere among the million stalks.

And as I paused to hear his song
    While swift the sunny moments slid,
Perhaps his mate sat listening long,
    And listened longer than I did.

Spring

GERARD MANLEY HOPKINS

Nothing is so beautiful as spring –
     When weeds, in wheels, shoot long and lovely and
          lush;
     Thrush's eggs look little low heavens, and thrush
Through the echoing timber does so rinse and wring
The ear, it strikes like lightnings to hear him sing.

Larks

KATHERINE TYNAN

All day in exquisite air
The song clomb an invisible stair,
Flight on flight, story on story,
Into the dazzling glory.

There was no bird, only a singing,
Up in the glory, climbing and ringing,
Like a small golden cloud at even,
Trembling 'twixt earth and heaven.

I saw no staircase, winding, winding,
Up in the dazzle, sapphire and blinding,
Yet round by round, in exquisite air,
The song went up the stair.

Prayers in a Field

MARGARET STANLEY-WRENCH

Like a handful of grain the words of blessing scatter
Over the cornfield. The callow heads of choirboys
Blond as dandelion cotton are ruffled by the wind,
And round their legs in a magpie whirl of black
And white plumage, cassock and surplice struggle,
Then everything holds its breath. A horse looks up
With mild, long cello face. A calf as red
As rusty iron chews over the day's cud
In this green evening. And then, like an upblown leaf
A lark twists, trembles, unfurls in crystal singing,
Bright notes, sharp facets, like rain-washed poplar leaves.
Upwards, onwards it flies, with the little rags
And tags and cotton-ends of our thoughts and prayers,
Our humble, pitiful words clinging, as tufts
Of dandelion clutch at the passer-by.
How clean, how sure is that simplicity
Of a bird's song! And yet, in the ear of God
Which rings more clearly, that or the halting words
Of man, whose fallible breath is warm with love?

'Here's the Spring back!'

ROBERT BROWNING

Here's the spring back or close,
When the almond-blossom blows:
    We shall have the word
    In a minor third
There is none but the cuckoo knows: . . .

(from *A Lovers' Quarrel*)

The Redbreast

ANTHONY RYE

The redbreast smoulders in the waste of snow :
His eye is large and bright, and to and fro
He draws and draws his slender threads of sound
Between the dark boughs and the freezing ground.

The Birds

MARGARET STANLEY-WRENCH

A lark's song is the whitening seed of harvests
Winnowed by the sun;
Nightingales remember the cold and the empty
Silences of the moon.

Thrushes sing of the storm and the bare branch gashing
An ash-grey sky;
Blackbirds call through the echoing coverts of evening,
Green summer in their cry.

Sparrows cluster, brown husks clogging trees;
And the wren is a fountain;
The robin tells of autumn and the mild
Spode touch of the rain.

Drowsy hens murmur of heat, and drool, and dream
In the dusty sun.
But a cock's cry is the sharpened scimitar
That gathers in the dawn.

Two Wonderful Things

BOOK OF PROVERBS

The way of an eagle in the air;
The way of a serpent upon a rock.

The Serpent

PERCY BYSSHE SHELLEY

Wake the serpent not – lest he
Should not know the way to go –
Let him crawl which yet lies sleeping
Through the deep grass of the meadow!
Not a bee shall hear him creeping,
Not a may-fly shall awaken
From its cradling blue-bell shaken,
Not the starlight as he's sliding
Through the grass with silent gliding.

Through the Year

JOHN KEATS

Thou shalt see the field-mouse peep
Meagre from its celled sleep;
And the snake all winter-thin
Cast on sunny banks its skin;
Freckled nest-eggs thou shalt see
Hatching in the hawthorn tree,
When the hen-bird's wing doth rest
Quiet on her mossy nest;
Then the hurry and alarm
When the beehive casts its swarm;
Acorns ripe down-pattering
While the autumn breezes sing.

(from *To Fancy*)

Flo, the White Duck

GWEN DUNN

All white and smooth is Flo
A-swimming;
Her lovely dress is plain . . .
No trimming.
A neat delight,
She fans to left and right
The silver-rippled pond.
Behind her, safe and fond,
Her yellow ducklings bob and skim,
Yellow, fluffy, trim.

But all a-waddle and a-spraddle goes Flo
A-walking;
A clacking voice she has
For talking.
In slimy ooze
She plants enormous shoes
And squelches, squat and slow.
Behind her in a row
Her ducklings dip and paddle
And try to spraddle.

Home Pictures in May

JOHN CLARE

The sunshine bathes in clouds of many hues
And morning's feet are gemmed with early dews;
Warm daffodils about the garden beds
Peep through their pale slim leaves their golden heads,
Sweet earthly suns of spring; the gosling broods,
In coats of sunny green, about the road
Waddle in ecstasy; and in rich moods
The old hen leads her flickering chicks abroad,
Oft scuttling 'neath her wings to see the kite
Hang wavering o'er them in the spring's blue light.
The sparrows round their new nests chirp with glee
And sweet the robin spring's young luxury shares,
Tootling its song in feathery gooseberry tree
While watching worms the gardener's spade unbares.

A Stream

JOHN KEATS

. . . Swarms of minnows show their little heads,
Staying their wavy bodies 'gainst the streams,
To taste the luxury of sunny beams
Temper'd with coolness. How they ever wrestle
With their own sweet delight, and ever nestle
Their silver bellies on the pebbly sand!
If you but scantily hold out the hand,
That very instant not one will remain;
But turn your eye, and they are there again.

(from *I stood tip-toe upon a little hill*)

The Lark in the Morn

As I was a-walking
One morning in the spring,
I met a pretty maiden
So sweetly she did sing.
And as we were a-walking
These words she did say,
'There's no life like the ploughboy's
All in the month of May.

'The lark in the morn
She doth rise up from her nest,
And mounts upon the air
With the dew all on her breast.
And like the pretty ploughboy
She doth whistle and doth sing,
And at night she doth return
To her own nest back again.'

Butterfly

S. THOMAS ANSELL

Down the air
    He falls sun-lazy
Debonair
    Upon a daisy;

Now he drifts
    To fall between
Snowy rifts
    Of scented bean;

And where petals
    Lift in flight,
There he settles
    Hid from sight.

Mrs Peck-Pigeon

ELEANOR FARJEON

Mrs Peck-Pigeon
Is pecking for bread,
Bob–bob–bob
Goes her little round head.
Tame as a pussy-cat
In the street,
Step–step–step
Go her little red feet.
With her little red feet
And her little round head,
Mrs Peck-Pigeon
Goes pecking for bread.

Black Lamb

ELEANOR GLENN WALLIS

All legs, tight curls of wool,
    A raucous bleat,
He staggers to his mother's
    Milky teat.

And as he sucks,
    His infant tail awry
Records the rhythm
    Of a lamb gone dry.

The Fur Coat

JAMES STEPHENS

I walked out in my Coat of Pride;
I looked about on every side;

And said the mountains should not be
Just where they were, and that the sea

Was out of place, and that the beech
Should be an oak! And then, from each,

I turned in dignity, as if
They were not there! I sniffed a sniff;

And climbed upon my sunny shelf;
And sneezed a while; and scratched myself.

The Bullfinch

BETTY HUGHES

I saw upon a winter's day
A bullfinch on a hedgerow spray;
He piped one note.
And since the countryside was mute,
As pure as rain I heard the flute
Of that small throat.

He picked a rotting willow-seed;
He whistled, in his joy to feed,
A whole sweet stave.
His sloe-black head, how shining sleek,
How strong his blunted sooty beak,
His eye, how brave!

Then boldly down he came to drink
Out of a roadside puddle's brink,
Half ice, half mud;
So coral-breasted, sturdy, merry,
That I forgave him plum and cherry
Nipped in the bud.

The Ant

Go to the ant, thou sluggard,
Consider her ways, and be wise:
Which, having no chief,
Overseer, or ruler,
Provideth her meat in the summer,
And gathereth her food in the harvest.

Bees

V. SACKVILLE-WEST

. . . In February, if the days be clear,
The waking bee, still drowsy on the wing,
Will guess the opening of another year
And blunder out to seek another spring.
Crashing through winter sunlight's pallid gold,
His clumsiness sets catkins on the willow
Shaking like lambs' tails in the early fold,
Dusting with pollen all his brown and yellow,
But when the rimy afternoon turns cold
And undern squalls buffet the chilly fellow,
He'll seek the hive's warm waxen welcoming
And set about the chambers' classic mould.

And then pell-mell his harvest follows swift,
Blossom and borage, lime and balm and clover,
On Downs the thyme, on cliffs the scantling thrift.
Everywhere bees go racing with the hours,
For every bee becomes a drunken lover,
Standing upon his head to sup the flowers.
All over England, from Northumbrian coasts,
To the wild sea-pink blown on Devon rocks,
Over the merry southern gardens, over
The grey-green beanfields, round the Kentish oasts,
Through the frilled spires of cottage hollyhocks,
Go the big brown fat bees, and wander in

Where dusty spears of sunlight cleave the barn,
And seek the sun again, and storm the whin,
And in the warm meridian solitude
Hum in the heather round the moorland tarn. . . .

(from *The Land*)

Bees' Kingdom

WILLIAM SHAKESPEARE

For so work the honey bees;
Creatures that, by a rule in nature, teach
The act of order to a peopled kingdom.
They have a king, and officers of sorts:
Where some, like magistrates, correct at home;
Others, like merchants, venture trade abroad;
Others, like soldiers, armed in their stings,
Make boot upon the summer's velvet buds;
Which pillage they with merry march bring home
To the tent-royal of their emperor:
Who, busied in his majesty, surveys
The singing masons building roofs of gold;
The civil citizens kneading up the honey;
The poor mechanic porters crowding in
Their heavy burdens at his narrow gate;
The sad-ey'd justice, with his surly hum,
Delivering o'er to executors pale
The lazy yawning drone.

(from *King Henry the Fifth*)

The Kangaroo

AUTHOR UNKNOWN

Old Jumpety-Bumpety-Hop-and-Go-One
Was lying asleep on his side in the sun.
This old Kangaroo, he was whisking the flies
(With his long glossy tail) from his ears and his eyes.
Jumpety-Bumpety-Hop-and-Go-One
Was lying asleep on his side in the sun,
Jumpety-Bumpety-Hop!

Squirrel

JOHN BUXTON

I saw a squirrel
Run through the wood.
By every tree
It stopped; and stood
Ready to climb,
With its paws on the trunk,
And every time
(For no danger came)
It hurried on,
And was gone.

Young Reynard

GEORGE MEREDITH

Gracefullest leaper, the dappled fox-cub
Curves over brambles with berries and buds,
Light as a bubble that flies from the tub,
Whisked by the laundry-wife out of her suds.
Wavy he comes, woolly, all at his ease,
Elegant, fashioned to foot with the deuce;
Nature's own prince of the dance: then he sees
Me, and retires as if making excuse.

Jenny Wren

W. H. DAVIES

Her sight is short. She comes quite near;
A foot to me's a mile to her;
And she is known as Jenny Wren,
The smallest bird in England. When
I heard that little bird at first,
Methought her frame would surely burst
With earnest song. Oft had I seen
Her running under leaves so green,
Or in the grass when fresh and wet,
As though her wings she would forget.
And, seeing this, I said to her –
'My pretty runner, you prefer
To be a thing to run unheard
Through leaves and grass, and not a bird!'
'Twas then she burst, to prove me wrong,
Into a sudden storm of song;
So very loud and earnest, I
Feared she would break her heart and die.
'Nay, nay,' I laughed, 'be you no thing
To run unheard, sweet scold, but sing!
O I could hear your voice near me,
Above the din in that oak tree,
When almost all the twigs on top
Had starlings singing without stop.'

WALTER DE LA MARE

Clapping her platter stood plump Bess,
And all across the green
Came scampering in, on wing and claw,
Chicken fat and lean : –
Dorking, Spaniard, Cochin China,
Bantams sleek and small,
Like feathers blown in a great wind,
They came at Bessie's call.

Melampus

GEORGE MEREDITH

With love exceeding a simple love of the things
That glide in grasses and rubble of woody wreck;
Or change their perch on a beat of quivering wings
From branch to branch, only restful to pipe and peck;
Or, bristled, curl at a touch their snouts in a ball;
Or cast their web between bramble and thorny hook;
The good physician Melampus, loving them all,
Among them walked, as a scholar who reads a book.

The Pigs and the Charcoal Burner

WALTER DE LA MARE

The old Pig said to the little pigs,
    'In the forest is truffles and mast,
Follow me then, all ye little pigs,
    Follow me fast!'

The Charcoal-burner sat in the shade,
    His chin on his thumb,
And saw the big Pig and the little pigs,
    Chuffling come.

He watched 'neath a green and giant bough,
    And the pigs in the ground
Made a wonderful grisling and gruzzling
    And greedy sound.

And when, full-fed, they were gone, and Night
    Walked her starry ways,
He stared with his cheeks in his hands
    At his sullen blaze.

The Little Mouse

PADRAIC COLUM

The little mouse
Climbed the candlestick
To eat the tallow
Around the wick.

But when he got up,
He could not get down;
He called his grandmother,
But she was gone.

Then he turned himself
Into a ball,
His little sharp nose
And tail and all,

And rolled right down
Without any fuss,
And went some place else,
That little mouse!

Welcome and Unwelcome Beasts

Ride Away

Ride away, ride away,
Johnny shall ride,
And he shall have pussy-cat
Tied to one side.
He shall have little dog
Tied to the other,
And Johnny shall ride
To see his grandmother.

'If no-one ever marries me'

LAURENCE ALMA-TADEMA

If no-one ever marries me –
And I don't see why they should;
For nurse says I'm not pretty,
And I'm seldom very good –

If no-one ever marries me
I shan't mind very much;
I shall buy a squirrel in a cage,
And a little rabbit hutch.

I shall have a cottage near a wood,
And a pony all my own.
And a little lamb quite clean and tame
That I can take to town.

And when I'm getting really old,
At twenty-eight or nine,
I shall buy a little orphan girl
And bring her up as mine.

The Bandog

WALTER DE LA MARE

Has anybody seen my Mopser? –
    A comely dog is he,
With hair of the colour of a Charles the Fifth,
    And teeth like ships at sea,
His tail it curls straight upwards,
    His ears stand two abreast,
And he answers to the simple name of Mopser,
    When civilly addressed.

Tim, an Irish Terrier

WINIFRED LETTS

It's wonderful dogs they're breeding now:
Small as a flea or large as a cow;
But my old dog Tim he'll never be bet
By any dog that he ever met.
'Come on,' says he, 'for I'm not kilt yet.'

No matter the size of the dog he'll meet,
Tim trails his coat along the street,
D'ye mind his scars an' his ragged ear,
The like of a Dublin fusilier?
He's a massacree dog that knows no fear.

But he'd stick to me till his latest breath;
An' he'd go with me to the gates of death.
He'd wait for a thousand years, maybe,
Scratchin' the door an' whinin' for me
If I myself were inside in Purgatory.

So I laugh when I hear thim make it plain
That dogs and men never meet again.
For all their talk who'd listen to thim,
With the soul in the shining eyes of him?
Would God be wasting a dog like Tim?

Irish Harper

THOMAS CAMPBELL

On the green banks of Shannon, when Sheelagh was
    nigh,
No blithe Irish lad was so happy as I;
No harp like my own could so cheerily play,
And wherever I went was my poor dog Tray.

When at last I was forced from my Sheelagh to part
She said – while the sorrow was big at her heart:
'Oh, remember your Sheelagh when far, far away,
And be kind, my dear Pat, to our poor dog Tray.'

Poor dog, he was faithful and kind, to be sure,
And he constantly loved me although I was poor;
When the sour-looking folks sent me heartless away,
I had always a friend in my poor dog Tray.

When the road was so dark and the night was so cold,
And Pat and his dog were grown weary and old,
How snugly we slept in my old coat of grey,
And he licked me for kindness – my old dog Tray.

Though my wallet was scant I remembered his case,
Nor refused my last crust to his pitiful face;
But he died at my feet on a cold winter's day,
And I played a sad lament for my poor dog Tray.

Where now shall I go, poor, forsaken, and blind?
Can I find one to guide me so faithful and kind?
To my sweet native village, so far, far away,
I can never more return with my poor dog Tray.

'I love little Pussy'

NURSERY RHYME

I love little pussy, her coat is so warm,
And if I don't hurt her she'll do me no harm.
So I'll not pull her tail nor drive her away,
But pussy and I very gently will play.
She'll sit by my side, and I'll give her some food,
And she'll love me because I am gentle and good.

On a Cat Ageing

ALEXANDER GRAY

He blinks upon the hearth-rug
And yawns in deep content,
Accepting all the comforts
That Providence has sent.

Louder he purrs, and louder,
In one glad hymn of praise
For all the night's adventures,
For quiet, restful days.

Life will go on for ever,
With all that cat can wish:
Warmth and the glad procession
Of fish and milk and fish.

Only – the thought disturbs him –
He's noticed once or twice,
The times are somehow breeding
A nimbler race of mice.

A Child's Dream

FRANCES CORNFORD

I had a little dog, and my dog was very small;
He licked me in the face, and he answered to my call;
Of all the treasures that were mine, I loved him most of
all.

His nose was fresh as morning dew and blacker than the
night;
I thought that it could even snuff the shadows and the
light;
And his tail he held bravely, like a banner in a fight.

His body covered thick with hair was very good to smell;
His little stomach underneath was pink as any shell;
And I loved him and honoured him, more than words
can tell.

We ran out in the morning, both of us, to play,
Up and down across the fields for all the sunny day;
But he ran so swiftly – he ran right away.

I looked for him, I called for him, entreatingly. Alas,
The dandelions could not speak, though they had seen
him pass,
And nowhere was his waving tail among the waving
grass.

I called him in a thousand ways and yet he did not come;
The pathways and the hedges were horrible and dumb.
I prayed to God who never heard. My desperate soul
grew numb.

The sun sank low. I ran; I prayed: 'If God has not the
power
To find him, let me die. I cannot bear another hour.'
When suddenly I came upon a great yellow flower.

And all among its petals, such was Heaven's grace,
In that golden hour, in that golden place,
All among its petals, was his hairy face.

Honey for tea

ELEANOR FARJEON

Buzzing bee,
Buzz away, bee,
To fill the comb
For the children's tea.
Humming bee,
Bee, hum home,
To fill the cells
In the honeycomb.

All the flowers in the garden
Have emptied their bells
Into the waxen
Honey-cells,
Larkspur and lupin
And marigold,
The bag of the bee
No more can hold.

All the babes in the nursery
With sweet sticky lips
Are sucking their thumbs
And finger-tips.
Susie and Sally
And Bobby and Bill
Can eat no more,
They have had their fill.

Hickety Pickety

NURSERY RHYME

Hickety, pickety, my black hen,
She lays eggs for gentlemen;
Sometimes nine and sometimes ten,
Hickety, pickety, my black hen.

PADRAIC COLUM

'I know where I'd get
An ass that would do,
If I had the money –
A pound or two,'

Said a ragged man
To my uncle one day;
He got the money
And went on his way.

And after that time
In market or fair
I'd look at the asses
That might be there.

And wonder what kind
Of an ass would do
For a ragged man
With a pound or two.

The Ride

As I ride, as I ride,
Ne'er has spur my swift horse plied,
Yet his hide, streaked and pied,
As I ride, as I ride,
Shows where sweat has sprung and dried,
– Zebra-footed, ostrich-thighed –
How has vied stride with stride
As I ride, as I ride!

(from *Through the Metidja to Abd-el-Kadr*)

Bird or Beast?

CHRISTINA ROSSETTI

Did any bird come flying
    After Adam and Eve,
When the door was shut against them
    And they sat down to grieve?

I think not Eve's peacock
    Splendid to see,
And I think not Adam's eagle
    But a dove may be.

Did any beast come pushing
    Through the thorny hedge
Into the thorny thistly world,
    Out from Eden's edge?

I think not a lion,
    Though his strength is such;
But an innocent loving lamb
    May have done as much.

If the dove preached from her bough,
    And the lamb from his sod,
The lamb and the dove
    Were preachers sent from God.

Valentine

F. ANDREWES

Come, be my valentine !
I'll gather eglantine,
Cowslips and sops-in-wine,
　　With fragrant roses;
Down by thy Phyllis sit,
She will white lilies get,
And daffadillies fit
　　To make thee posies.

I have a milk-white lamb
New taken from the dam,
It comes where'er I am
　　When I call 'Willie'.
I have a wanton kid
Under my apron hid,
A colt that ne'er was rid,
　　A pretty filly.

I bear, in sign of love,
A sparrow in my glove,
And in my breast a dove,
　　These shall be all thine;
Besides, of sheep a flock
Which yieldeth many a lock,
And that shall be thy stock –
　　Come, be my valentine !

ANONYMOUS

If you should meet a crocodile,
 Don't take a stick and poke him;
Ignore the welcome in his smile,
 Be careful not to stroke him.
For as he sleeps upon the Nile,
 He thinner gets and thinner;
And whene'er you meet a crocodile
 He's ready for his dinner.

Snake

EMILY DICKINSON

A narrow fellow in the grass
Occasionally rides;
You may have met him – did you not?
His notice sudden is.

The grass divides as with a comb,
A spotted shaft is seen;
And then it closes at your feet
And opens further on.

He likes a boggy acre,
A floor too cool for corn.
Yet when a child, and barefoot,
I more than once, at morn,

Have passed, I thought, a whip-lash
Unbraiding in the sun –
When, stopping to secure it,
It wrinkled, and was gone.

Several of nature's people
I know, and they know me;
I feel for them a transport
Of cordiality;

But never met this fellow,
Attended or alone,
Without a tighter breathing,
And zero at the bone.

Kilkenny Cats

AUTHOR UNKNOWN

There once were two cats of Kilkenny
Each thought there was one cat too many;
So they fought and they fit,
And they scratched and they bit,
Till, excepting their nails
And the tips of their tails,
Instead of two cats there weren't any.

The Little Mouse

AUTHOR UNKNOWN

I have seen you, little mouse,
Running all about the house,
Through the hole your little eye
In the wainscot peeping sly,
Hoping soon some crumbs to steal,
To make quite a hearty meal.
Look before you venture out,
See if pussy is about;
If she's gone you'll quickly run
To the larder for some fun;
Round about the dishes creep;
Taking into each a peep,
To choose the daintiest that's there,
Spoiling things you do not care.

Two Little Kittens

AUTHOR UNKNOWN

Two little kittens, one stormy night,
Began to quarrel, and then to fight.
One had a mouse, the other had none,
And that's the way the quarrel began.

'I'll have that mouse,' said the bigger cat.
'*You'll* have that mouse? We'll see about that!'
'I *will* have that mouse!' said the older one.
'You *shan't* have the mouse!' said the little one.

I told you before 'twas a stormy night
When those two little kittens began to fight.
The old woman seized her sweeping broom,
And swept the two kittens right out of the room.

The ground was all covered with frost and snow,
And the two little kittens had nowhere to go.
So they laid them down on the mat at the door,
While the old woman finished sweeping the floor.

Then they both crept in as quiet as mice,
All wet with the snow and as cold as ice.
For they found it much better that stormy night
To lie down and sleep, than to quarrel and fight.

The Rhinoceros

OGDEN NASH

The rhino is a homely beast,
For human eyes he's not a feast,
But you and I will never know
Why nature chose to make him so.
Farewell, farewell, you old rhinoceros,
I'll stare at something less prepocerous!

The Frog

HILAIRE BELLOC

Be kind and tender to the Frog,
And do not call him names,
As 'Slimy skin', or 'Polly-wog',
Or otherwise 'Ugly James',
Or 'Gap-a-grin', or 'Toad-gone wrong',
Or 'Billy Bandy-knees'.
The Frog is justly sensitive
To epithets like these.
No animal will more repay
A treatment kind and fair;
At least so lonely people say
Who keep a frog (and, by the way,
They are extremely rare).

Sonnet to a Cat

JOHN KEATS

Cat! who has pass'd thy grand climacteric,
   How many mice and rats hast in thy days
   Destroy'd? – How many tit-bits stolen? Gaze
With those bright languid segments green, and prick
Those velvet ears – but pr'ythee do not stick
   Thy latent talons in me – and upraise
   Thy gentle mew – and tell me all thy frays
Of fish and mice, and rats and tender chick.
Nay, look not down, nor lick thy dainty wrists –
   For all the wheezy asthma – and for all
Thy tail's tip is nick'd off – and though the fists
   Of many a maid have given thee many a maul,
Still is that fur as soft as when the lists
   In youth thou enter'dst on glass bottled wall.

The Little Crocodile

How doth the little crocodile
  Improve his shining tail,
And pour the waters of the Nile
  On every golden scale!

How cheerfully he seems to grin,
  How neatly spreads his claws,
And welcomes little fishes in
  With gently smiling jaws!

Rats!

ROBERT BROWNING

Rats!
They fought the dogs and killed the cats,
    And bit the babies in the cradles,
And ate the cheeses out of the vats,
    And licked the soup from the cook's own ladles,
Split open the kegs of salted sprats,
Made nests inside men's Sunday hats,
And even spoiled the women's chats,
        By drowning their speaking
        With shrieking and squeaking
In fifty different sharps and flats.

(from *The Pied Piper of Hamelin*)

The Rum Tum Tugger

T. S. ELIOT

The Rum Tum Tugger is a Curious Cat.
If you offer him pheasant he would rather have grouse.
If you put him in a house he would much prefer a flat,
If you put him in a flat then he'd rather have a house.
If you set him on a mouse then he only wants a rat,
If you set him on a rat then he'd rather chase a mouse.
Yes the Rum Tum Tugger is a Curious Cat –
    And there isn't any call for me to shout it:
      For he will do
      As he do do
         And there's no doing anything about it!

The Rum Tum Tugger is a terrible bore:
When you let him in then he wants to be out;
He's always on the wrong side of every door,
And as soon as he's at home, then he'd like to get about.
He likes to lie in the bureau drawer,
But he makes such a fuss if he can't get out.
Yes the Rum Tum Tugger is a Curious Cat –
    And there isn't any use for you to doubt it:
      For he will do
      As he do do
         And there's no doing anything about it!

The Rum Tum Tugger is a curious beast:
His disobliging ways are a matter of habit.
If you offer him fish then he always wants a feast;
When there isn't any fish then he won't eat rabbit.
If you offer him cream then he sniffs and sneers,
For he only likes what he finds for himself;
So you'll catch him in it right up to the ears,
If you put it away on the larder shelf.
The Rum Tum Tugger is artful and knowing,
The Rum Tum Tugger doesn't care for a cuddle;
But he'll leap on your lap in the middle of your sewing,
For there's nothing he enjoys like a horrible muddle.
Yes the Rum Tum Tugger is a Curious Cat —
    And there isn't any need for me to spout it:
        For he will do
        As he do do
            And there's no doing anything about it!

Loving-Kindness

'If I had a Donkey'

If I had a donkey
That wouldn't go,
D'you think I'd wallop him?
No! No! No!
I'd put him in a stable
And keep him nice and warm,
The best little donkey
That ever was born.
Gee up, Neddy,
Gee up, Neddy,
The best little donkey
That ever was born.

Sing-Song

CHRISTINA ROSSETTI

Bread and milk for breakfast,
    And woollen frocks to wear,
And a crumb for robin redbreast
    On the cold days of the year.

The Donkey

GERTRUDE HIND

I saw a donkey
    One day old,
His head was too big
    For his neck to hold;
His legs were shaky
    And long and loose,
They rocked and staggered
    And weren't much use.
He tried to gambol
    And frisk a bit,
But he wasn't quite sure
    Of the trick of it.
His queer little coat
    Was soft and grey
And curled at his neck
    In a lovely way.
His face was wistful
    And left no doubt
That he felt life needed
    Some thinking out.
So he blundered round
    In venturous quest,
And then lay flat
    On the ground to rest.

He looked so little
        And weak and slim,
I prayed the world
        Might be good to him.

Cats

FRANCIS SCARFE

Those who love cats which do not even purr,
Or which are thin and tired and very old,
Bend down to them in the street and stroke their fur
And rub their ears and smooth their breast, and hold
Their paws, and gaze into their eyes of gold.

The Runaway

ROBERT FROST

Once when the snow of the year was beginning to fall,
We stopped by a mountain pasture to say 'Whose colt?'
A little Morgan had one forefoot on the wall,
The other curled at his breast. He dipped his head
And snorted to us. And then he had to bolt.
We heard the miniature thunder where he fled,
And we saw him, or thought we saw him, dim and grey,
Like a shadow against the curtain of falling flakes.
'I think the little fellow's afraid of the snow.
He isn't winter-broken. It isn't play
With the little fellow at all. He's running away.
I doubt if even his mother could tell him, "Sakes,
It's only weather." He'd think she didn't know!
Where is his mother? He can't be out alone.'
And now he comes again with clatter of stone,
And mounts the wall again with whited eyes
And all his tail that isn't hair up straight.
He shudders his coat as if to throw off flies.
'Whoever it is that leaves him out so late,
When other creatures have gone to stall and bin,
Ought to be told to come and take him in.'

'I Must Sell My Horse'

ELEANOR FARJEON

I must sell my horse because the skies are snowing,
Nothing in the cupboard, children crying on the floor.
Never was another horse like him for going;
I must sell my horse to keep the wolf from the door.
Friend, old friend, the children want their meat,
In another stable you'll have corn to eat.

Once he drew the rake that set the green hay flying,
Once he drew the cart that carried in the yellow corn,
Once I rode my horse because a man was dying,
Once I rode my horse because a child was born.
Friend, old friend, the children want their meat,
In another stable you'll have corn to eat.

Two Songs of a Fool

W. B. YEATS

I

A speckled cat and a tame hare
Eat at my hearthstone
And sleep there;
And both look up to me alone
For learning and defence
As I look up to Providence.

I start out of my sleep to think
Some day I may forget
Their food and drink;
Or, the house door left unshut,
The hare may run till it's found
The horn's sweet note and the tooth of the hound.

I bear a burden that might well try
Men that do all by rule,
And what can I
That am a wandering-witted fool
But pray to God that He ease
My great responsibilities?

II

I slept on my three-legged stool by the fire,
The speckled cat slept on my knee;
We never thought to enquire
Where the brown hare might be,
And whether the door were shut.

Who knows how she drank the wind
Stretched up on two legs from the mat,
Before she had settled her mind
To drum with her heel and to leap?
Had I but awakened from sleep
And called her name, she had heard,
It may be, and had not stirred,
That now, it may be, has found
The horn's sweet note and the tooth of the hound.

The Snare

JAMES·STEPHENS

I hear a sudden cry of pain!
    There is a rabbit in a snare;
Now I hear the cry again,
    But I cannot tell from where.

But I cannot tell from where
    He is calling out for aid;
Crying on the frightened air,
    Making everything afraid.

Making everything afraid,
    Wrinkling up his little face,
As he cries again for aid;
    And I cannot find the place!

And I cannot find the place
    Where his paw is in the snare:
Little one! Oh, little one!
    I am searching everywhere!

The Caterpillar

CHRISTINA ROSSETTI

Brown and furry
Caterpillar in a hurry,
Take your walk
To the shady leaf, or stalk,
    Or what not,
Which may be the chosen spot.
    No toad spy you,
Hovering bird of prey pass by you;
Spin and die,
To live again as butterfly.

Poor Dicky

AUTHOR UNKNOWN

Poor Dicky's dead! The bell we toll,
And lay him in the deep, dark hole.
The sun may shine, the clouds may rain,
But Dick will never pipe again.
His quilt will be as sweet as ours:
Bright buttercups and cuckoo flowers.

Days and Nights

A Boy's Song

JAMES HOGG

Where the pools are bright and deep,
Where the grey trout lies asleep,
Up the river and over the lea,
That's the way for Billy and me.

Where the blackbird sings the latest,
Where the hawthorn blooms the sweetest,
Where the nestlings chirp and flee,
That's the way for Billy and me.

Where the mowers mow the cleanest,
Where the hay lies thick and greenest,
There to track the homeward bee,
That's the way for Billy and me.

Father and I in the Woods

DAVID McCORD

'Son,'
My father used to say,
    'Don't run.'

    'Walk,'
My father used to say,
    'Don't talk.'

    'Words,'
My father used to say,
    'Scare birds.'

    So be:
It's sky and brook and bird
    And tree.

Winter Rains

R. C. TREVELYAN

When meals are glum and shoulders ache,
No match will strike or firewood blaze,
Fiddlestrings squeak and tempers break,
No robin sings and no hen lays;
When paths are pools, and noses pearled,
And cats in kitchen fenders curled
Dream of a happier, drier world;

Then suddenly, when least we think,
A bright wind breaks the mist, and there
The sun looks out above the brink
Of piled-up clouds, stair over stair:
Glad then at heart are all live things,
Both small and great, on feet or wings,
Birds, boys and beggars, cats and kings.

Summer

CHRISTINA ROSSETTI

Winter is cold-hearted,
    Spring is yea and nay,
Autumn is a weather-cock
        Blown every way.
    Summer days for me
When every leaf is on its tree.

    When Robin's not a beggar,
    And Jenny Wren's a bride,
And larks hang singing, singing, singing,
    Over the wheat-fields wide,
    And anchored lilies ride,
    And the pendulum spider
    Swings from side to side;

And blue-black beetles transact business,
    And gnats fly in a host,
And furry caterpillars hasten
    That no time be lost,
    And moths grow fat and thrive,
    And ladybirds arrive.

    Before green apples blush,
    Before green nuts embrown,
    Why one day in the country

137

Is worth a month in town;
Is worth a day and a year
Of the dusty, musty, lag-last fashion
That days drone elsewhere.

Waiting on a Hot Afternoon

GEORGE MEREDITH

Doves of the fir-wood, walling high our red roof.
Through the long noon coo, crooning through the coo.
Loose droop the leaves, and down the sleepy roadway
Sometimes pipes a chaffinch; loose droops the blue.
Cows flap a slow tail, knee-deep in the river,
Breathless, given up to sun and gnat and fly.
Nowhere is she seen; and if I see her nowhere,
Lightning may come, straight rains and tiger sky.

(from *Love in the Valley*)

The Barn

EDMUND BLUNDEN

All merry noise of hens astir
Or sparrows squabbling on the roof
Comes to the barn's broad open door;
You hear upon the stable floor
Old hungry Dapple strike his hoof,
And the blue fantail's whirr.

Now is the Time

ELIZABETH COATSWORTH

Now is the time
when robins call,
the fretful horse
stamps in the stall,
the cock claps wings
in orchards bare,
under the hedge
crouches the hare.

Now is the time
spring fires burn,
the air is sweet
with smouldering fern,
and through the quiet
hours of night
the gold-eyed frogs
creak with delight.

Autumn

JOHN KEATS

Where are the songs of Spring? Aye, where are they?
    Think not of them – thou hast thy music too,
While barred clouds bloom the soft-dying day
    And touch the stubble-plains with rosy hue;
Then in a wailful choir the small gnats mourn
    Among the river-sallows, borne aloft
        Or sinking as the light wind lives or dies;
    And full-grown lambs loud bleat from hilly bourn;
Hedge-crickets sing, and now with treble soft
The redbreast whistles from a garden-croft,
    And gathering swallows twitter in the skies.

(from *Ode to Autumn*)

'Tis Sweet

LORD BYRON

'Tis sweet to hear the watch-dog's honest bark
    Bay deep-mouthed welcome as we draw near home;
'Tis sweet to know there is an eye will mark
    Our coming, and look brighter when we come;
'Tis sweet to be awaken'd by the lark,
    Or lull'd by falling waters; sweet the hum
Of bees, the voice of girls, the song of birds,
The lisp of children, and their earliest words.

(from *Don Juan*)

The Barefoot Boy

JOHN GREENLEAF WHITTIER

O for boyhood's painless play,
Sleep that wakes in laughing day,
Health that mocks the doctor's rules,
Knowledge never learned of schools,
Of the wild bee's morning chase,
Of the wild-flower's time and place,
Flight of fowl and habitude
Of the tenants of the wood;
How the tortoise bears his shell,
How the woodchuck digs his cell,
And the ground-mole sinks his well;
How the robin feeds her young,
How the oriole's nest is hung;
Where the whitest lilies blow,
Where the freshest berries grow,
Where the ground-nut trails its vine,
Where the wood-grape's clusters shine;
Of the black wasp's cunning way,
Mason of his walls of clay,
And the architectural plans
Of grey hornet artisans!
For, eschewing books and tasks,
Nature answers all he asks;

Hand in hand with her he walks,
Face to face with her he talks,
Part and parcel of her joy –
Blessings on the barefoot boy !

Boy Fishing

E. J. SCOVELL

I am cold and alone,
On my tree-root sitting as still as stone.
The fish come to my net. I scorned the sun,
The voices on the road, and they have gone.
My eyes are buried in the cold pond, under
The cold, spread leaves; my thoughts are silver-wet.
I have ten stickleback, a half-day's plunder,
Safe in my jar. I shall have ten more yet.

Summer Evening

WALTER DE LA MARE

The sandy cat by the Farmer's chair
Mews at his knee for dainty fare;
Old Rover in his moss-greened house
Mumbles a bone, and barks at a mouse.
In the dewy fields the cattle lie
Chewing the cud 'neath a fading sky;
Dobbin at manger pulls his hay:
Gone is another summer's day.

The Fallow Deer at the Lonely House

THOMAS HARDY

One without looks in tonight
Through the curtain-chink
From the sheet of glistening white;
One without looks in tonight
As we sit and think
By the fender-brink.

We do not discern those eyes
Watching in the snow;
Lit by lamps of rosy dyes
We do not discern those eyes
Wondering, aglow,
Fourfooted, tiptoe.

Fireflies in the Garden

ROBERT FROST

Here come real stars to fill the upper skies,
And here on earth come emulating flies,
That though they never equal stars in size,
(And they were never really stars at heart)
Achieve at times a very star-like start.
Only, of course, they can't sustain the part.

The Mower to the Glow-Worms

ANDREW MARVELL

Ye living lamps, by whose dear light
    The nightingale does sit so late,
And, studying all the summer night,
    Her matchless songs does meditate;

Ye country comets, that portend
    No war, nor prince's funeral,
Shining into no higher end
    Than to presage the grasses' fall;

Ye glow-worms, whose officious flame
    To wandering mowers shows the way,
That in the night have lost their aim,
    And after foolish fires do stray;

Your courteous lights in vain you waste,
    Since Juliana here is come;
For she my mind hath so displaced
    That I shall never find my home.

Come In

ROBERT FROST

As I came to the edge of the woods,
Thrush music – hark!
Now if it was dusk outside,
Inside it was dark.

Too dark in the woods for a bird
By sleight of wing
To better its perch for the night,
Though it still could sing.

The last of the light of the sun
That had died in the west
Still lived for one song more
In a thrush's breast.

Far in the pillared dark
Thrush music went –
Almost like a call to come in
To the dark and lament.

But no, I was out for stars:
I would not come in.
I meant not even if asked,
And I hadn't been.

Dusk

GEORGE MEREDITH

Lovely are the curves of the white owl sweeping
Wavy in the dusk lit by one large star.
Lone on the fir-branch, his rattle-note unvaried,
Brooding o'er the gloom, spins the brown eve-jar.

(from *Love in the Valley*)

Night Song

FRANCES CORNFORD

On moony nights the dogs bark shrill
Down the valley and up the hill.

There's one who is angry to behold
The moon so unafraid and cold,
That makes the earth as bright as day,
But yet unhappy, dead, and grey.

Another in his strawy lair,
Says: 'Who's a-howling over there?
By heavens I will stop him soon
From interfering with the moon.'

So back he barks, with throat upthrown;
'You leave our moon, our moon alone.'
And other distant dogs respond
Beyond the fields, beyond, beyond.

Out in the Dark

EDWARD THOMAS

Out in the dark over the snow
The fallow fawns invisible go
With the fallow doe;
And the winds blow
Fast as the stars are slow.

Stealthily the dark haunts round
And, when a lamp goes, without a sound
At a swifter bound
Than the swiftest hound,
Arrives, and all else is drowned;

And I and star and wind and deer
Are in the dark together – near,
Yet far – and fear
Drums on my ear
In that sage company drear.

How weak and little is the light,
All the universe of sight,
Love and delight,
Before the might,
If you love it not, of night.

The Cart-Horses

EDEN PHILLPOTTS

'Twixt two and three upon a silent night
As earth rolled dreaming in the full-mooned tide,
Slow hooves came thud and thud: there hove in sight
Black horses twain, that wandered side by side.
Two great cart-horses, looming giant large,
Enjoyed their rest. Each to the other spoke,
Then bent and drank beside a streamlet's marge,
While moonlight found their lustrous eyes and woke
A glint of consciousness, a hint of mind.
Now they rubbed noses, shook their heavy manes,
Lifted their necks and neighed upon the wind,
Then fell to whispering, their little brains
Busy about shared interests, unshared
By those for whom their strenuous time was spent.
One something said, whereat the other stared,
Then started galloping, then off they went,
To vanish on the far, night-hidden heath;
And well I knew they were exchanging thought,
Uttering strange, dim things with their sweet breath
Of which we busy, daylight folk know nought –
Views touching fate, under the still moonshine,
As near to truth, perchance, as yours, or mine.

Lullaby of a Woman of the Mountains

PADRAIC H. PEARSE

House, be still, and ye little grey mice,
Lie close tonight in your hidden lairs.

Moths on the window, fold your wings,
Little black chafers, silence your humming.

Plover and curlew, fly not over my house,
Do not speak, wild barnacle, passing over the mountain.

Things of the mountain that wake in the night-time,
Do not stir tonight till the daylight whitens!

Lullaby of the Fairies of the Wood

WILLIAM SHAKESPEARE

You spotted snakes with double tongue
    Thorny hedgehogs, be not seen;
Newts and blind-worms, do no wrong,
    Come not near our fairy queen.

Weaving spiders, come not here;
    Hence, you long-legg'd spinners, hence!
Beetles black, approach not near;
    Worm nor snail, do no offence.

(from *A Midsummer Night's Dream*)

A Witches' Charm

BEN JONSON

The owl is abroad, the bat and the toad,
    And so is the cat a-mountain;
The ant and the mole sit both in a hole,
    And the frog peeps out o' the fountain.
The dogs they do bay, and the timbrels play,
    The spindle is now a-turning;
The moon it is red, and the stars are fled,
    But all the sky is a-burning.

Cock-crow

EDWARD THOMAS

Out of the wood of thoughts that grows by night
To be cut down by the sharp axe of light –
Out of the night, two cocks together crow,
Cleaving the darkness with a silver blow:
And bright before my eyes twin trumpeters stand,
Heralds of splendour, one at either hand,
Each facing each as in a coat of arms:
The milkers lace their boots up at the farms.

The Owl

ALFRED, LORD TENNYSON

When cats run home and light is come,
    And dew is cold upon the ground,
And the far-off stream is dumb,
    And the whirring sail goes round,
    And the whirring sail goes round;
        Alone and warming his five wits,
        The white owl in the belfry sits.

When merry milkmaids click the latch,
    And rarely smells the new-mown hay,
And the cock hath sung beneath the thatch
    Twice or thrice his roundelay,
    Twice or thrice his roundelay;
        Alone and warming his five wits,
        The white owl in the belfry sits.

Special Moments

Richness

V. SACKVILLE-WEST

My life was rich; I took a swarm of bees
And found a crumpled snake-skin on the road,
All in one day, and was increased by these.

(from *The Land*)

ROBERT BROWNING

Ah, did you once see Shelley plain,
    And did he stop and speak to you,
And did you speak to him again?
    How strange it seems and new!

But you were living before that,
    And also you are living after;
And the memory I started at –
    My starting moves your laughter.

I crossed a moor, with a name of its own
    And a certain use in the world no doubt,
Yet a hand's-breadth of it shines alone
    'Mid the blank miles round about:

For there I picked up on the heather
    And there I put inside my breast
A moulted feather, an eagle-feather!
    Well, I forget the rest!

Four Ducks on a Pond

WILLIAM ALLINGHAM

Four ducks on a pond,
A grass bank beyond,
A blue sky of spring,
White clouds on the wing;
What a little thing
To remember for years –
To remember with tears.

Adlestrop

EDWARD THOMAS

Yes. I remember Adlestrop –
The name, because one afternoon
Of heat the express-train drew up there
Unwontedly. It was late June.

The steam hissed. Someone cleared his throat.
No one left and no one came
On the bare platform. What I saw
Was Adlestrop – only the name,

And willows, willow-herb, and grass,
And meadowsweet and haycocks dry,
No whit less still and lonely fair
Than the high cloudlets in the sky.

And for that minute a blackbird sang
Close by, and round him, mistier,
Farther and farther, all the birds
Of Oxfordshire and Gloucestershire.

TERESA HOOLEY

Today I saw a butterfly,
    The first-born of the spring,
Sunning itself upon a bank –
    A lovely tawny thing.

I saw a dandelion, too,
    As golden as the sun;
And these will still be beautiful
    When all the wars are done.

A Great Time

W. H. DAVIES

Sweet Chance, that led my steps abroad,
    Beyond the town, where wild flowers grow –
A rainbow and a cuckoo, Lord,
    How rich and great the times are now!
        Know, all ye sheep
        And cows that keep
On staring that I stand so long
    In grass that's wet from heavy rain –
A rainbow and a cuckoo's song
    May never come together again;
        May never come
        This side the tomb.

'Wild Bees had Built...'

W. W. GIBSON

Wild bees had built, while we had been from home,
A nest inside of the big old-fashioned lock
Of the cottage door; and choked it so with wax
The key wouldn't turn in the wards; and we'd to climb
Into our home across the window-sill.
They must have started as soon as we'd turned our backs,
And set about their labour with right good will,
To have made themselves so secure in the nest, and block
The wards so badly in so short a time:
For they'd even started filling the honeycomb.

Yet, as we entered our little house once more,
It seemed to us not only the wild bees
Had been at work: for we found in each room a store
Of honeyed delight and golden memories.

Dust of Snow

ROBERT FROST

The way a crow
Shook down on me
The dust of snow
From a hemlock tree

Has given my heart
A change of mood
And saved some part
Of a day I had rued.

The Saffron Butterfly

TERESA HOOLEY

Out of its dark cocoon,
Like a blossom breaking earth
A saffron-wingéd butterfly
Came to its April birth,
Fluttered by banks of primroses:
I could not tell, not I,
If yellow butterflies starred the hedge,
Or a flower flew in the sky.

Colchis

TERESA HOOLEY

The sheep grazed on the hillside;
    Chill was the dawn breeze;
Like burning honey came up the sun
    Behind the bare black trees.

The flock was touched to glory;
    Somerset glowed to Greece:
With Argonaut eyes of vision
    I saw the Golden Fleece.

The Parrots

W. W. GIBSON

Somewhere, somewhere I've seen,
But where or when I'll never know,
Parrots of shrilly green
With crests of shriller scarlet flying
Out of black cedars as the sun was dying
    Against cold peaks of snow.

From what forgotten life
Of other worlds I cannot tell
Flashes that screeching strife:
Yet the shrill colour and the shrill crying
Sing through my blood and set my heart replying
    And jangling like a bell.

The Oxen

THOMAS HARDY

Christmas Eve, and twelve of the clock.
'Now they are all on their knees,'
An elder said as we sat in a flock
By the embers in hearthside ease.

We pictured the meek mild creatures where
They dwelt in their strawy pen,
Nor did it occur to one of us there
To doubt they were kneeling then.

So fair a fancy few would weave
In these years! Yet, I feel,
If someone said, on Christmas Eve,
'Come; see the oxen kneel,

In the lonely barton by yonder coomb
Our childhood used to know,'
I should go with him in the gloom,
Hoping it might be so.

Singled Out

ROBERT BROWNING

This is a spray the Bird clung to,
    Making it blossom with pleasure,
Ere the high tree-top she sprung to,
    Fit for her nest and her treasure.
    Oh, what a hope beyond measure
Was the poor spray's, which the flying feet hung to –
So to be singled out, built in, and sung to!

(from *Misconceptions*)

Different Lives

Eternity

WILLIAM BLAKE

He who bends to himself a joy
Doth the wingéd life destroy;
But he who kisses a joy as it flies
Lives in Eternity's sunrise.

'I had a Dove'

JOHN KEATS

I had a dove and the sweet dove died;
　　And I have thought it died of grieving:
O, what could it grieve for? Its feet were tied,
　　With a silken thread of my own hand's weaving;
Sweet little red feet! Why should you die –
Why should you leave me, sweet bird! Why?
You liv'd alone in the forest-tree,
Why, pretty thing! would you not live with me!
I kiss'd you oft and gave you white peas;
Why not live sweetly, as in the green trees?

Jack and his Pony, Tom

Jack had a little pony – Tom;
He frequently would take it from
The stable where it used to stand
And give it sugar with his hand.

He also gave it oats and hay
And carrots twenty times a day
And grass in basketfuls, and greens,
And swedes and mangolds, also beans,
And patent foods from various sources
And bread (which isn't good for horses)
And chocolate and apple-rings
And lots and lots of other things
The most of which do not agree
With Polo Ponies such as he.
And all in such a quantity
As ruined his digestion wholly
And turned him from a Ponopoly
– I mean a Polo Pony – into
A case that clearly must be seen to.

Because he swelled and swelled and swelled.
Which, when the kindly boy beheld,
He gave him medicine by the pail
And malted milk, and nutmeg ale,

And yet it only swelled the more
Until its stomach touched the floor.
And then it heaved and groaned as well
And staggered, till at last it fell
And found it could not rise again.
Jack wept and prayed – but all in vain.
The pony died, and as it died
Kicked him severely in the side.

Moral
Kindness to animals should be
Attuned to their brutality.

The Child with the Bird at the Bush

JOHN BUNYAN

My little bird, how canst thou sit
    And sing amidst so many thorns?
Let me but hold upon thee get,
    My love with honour thee adorns.

Thou art at present little worth,
    Five farthings none will give for thee;
But prithee, little bird, come forth,
    Thou of more value art to me.

'Tis true it is sun-shine today,
    Tomorrow birds will have a storm;
My pretty one, come thou away,
    My bosom then shall keep thee warm.

Thou subject art to cold o' nights,
    When darkness is thy covering;
At days thy danger's great by kites,
    How canst thou then sit there and sing?

Thy food is scarce and scanty too,
    'Tis worms and trash which thou dost eat;
Thy present state I pity do,
    Come, I'll provide thee better meat.

I'll feed thee with white bread and milk,
    And sugar-plums, if them thou crave;
I'll cover thee with finest silk,
    That from the cold I may thee save.

My father's palace shall be thine,
    Yea, in it thou shalt sit and sing;
My little bird, if thou'lt be mine,
    The whole year round shall be thy spring.

I'll teach thee all the notes at court;
    Unthought-of music thou shalt play;
And all that thither to resort
    Shall praise thee for it every day.

I'll keep thee safe from cat and cur,
    No manner o' harm shall come to thee:
Yea, I will be thy succourer,
    My bosom shall thy cabin be.

But lo ! behold, the bird is gone;
    These charmings would not make her yield:
The child's left at the bush alone,
    The bird flies yonder o'er the field.

The Little Bird

SYDNEY DOBELL

I had a little bird,
I took it from the nest;
I prest it, and blest it,
And nursed it in my breast.
I sat it on the ground,
I danced round and round,
And sang about it so cheerly,
With 'Hey my little bird, and ho my little bird,
And ho but I love thee dearly!'

I make a little feast,
Of food soft and sweet,
I hold it in my breast
And coax it to eat;

I pit, and I pat,
I call it this and that,
And sing about it so cheerly,
With 'Hey my little bird, and ho my little bird,
And ho but I love thee dearly!'

I may kiss, I may sing,
But I can't make it feed,
It taketh no heed
Of any pleasant thing.

I scolded, and I socked,
But it minded not a whit,
Its little mouth was locked,
And I could not open it.

Though with pit and with pat,
And with this, and with that,
I sang about it so cheerly,
And 'Hey my little bird, and ho my little bird,
And ho but I love thee dearly.'

But when the day was done,
And the room was at rest,
And I sat alone
With my birdie in my breast,

And the light had fled,
And not a sound was heard,
Then my little bird
Lifted up its head,

And the little mouth
Loosed its sullen pride,
And it opened, it opened,
With a yearning strong and wide.

Swifter than I speak
I brought it food once more,
But the poor little beak
Was locked as before.

I sat down again,
And not a creature stirred,
I laid the little bird
Again where it had lain;

And again when nothing stirred,
And not a word I said,
Then my little bird
Lifted up its head,
And the little beak
Loosed its stubborn pride,
And it opened, it opened,
With a yearning strong and wide.

It lay in my breast,
It uttered no cry,
'Twas famished, 'twas famished,
And I couldn't tell why.

I couldn't tell why,
But I saw that it would die,
For all that I kept dancing round and round,
And singing above it so cheerly,
With 'Hey my little bird, and ho my little bird,
And ho but I love thee dearly!'

No Shop does the Bird Use

ELIZABETH COATSWORTH

No shop does the bird use,
no counter nor baker,
but the bush is his orchard,
the grass is his acre,
the ant is his quarry,
the seed is his bread,
and a star is his candle
to light him to bed.

The Fly

WALTER DE LA MARE

How large unto the tiny fly
    Must little things appear ! –
A rosebud like a feather bed,
    Its prickle like a spear;

A dewdrop like a looking-glass,
    A hair like golden wire;
The smallest grain of mustard-seed
    As fierce as coals of fire;

A loaf of bread a lofty hill;
    A wasp, a cruel leopard;
And specks of salt as bright to see
    As lambkins to a shepherd.

On a Night of Snow

ELIZABETH COATSWORTH

Cat, if you go outdoors you must walk in the snow,
You will come back with little white shoes on your feet,
Little white slippers of snow that have heels of sleet.
Stay by the fire, my Cat. Lie still, do not go.
See how the flames are leaping and hissing low,
I will bring you a saucer of milk like a marguerite,
So white and so smooth, so spherical and so sweet –
Stay with me, Cat. Out-doors the wild winds blow.

Out-doors the wild winds blow, Mistress, and dark is the
        night.
Strange voices cry in the trees, intoning strange lore
And more than cats move, lit by our eyes' green light,
On silent feet where the meadow grasses hang hoar –
Mistress, there are portents abroad of magic and might,
And things that are yet to be done. Open the door!

The Greater Cats

V. SACKVILLE-WEST

The greater cats with golden eyes
Stare out between the bars.
Deserts are there, and different skies,
And night with different stars.

Furry Bear

A. A. MILNE

If I were a bear
 And a big bear too,
I shouldn't much care
 If it froze or snew;
I shouldn't much mind
 If it snowed or friz –
I'd be all fur-lined
 With a coat like his!

For I'd have fur boots and a brown fur wrap,
And brown fur knickers and a big fur cap.
I'd have a fur muffle-ruff to cover my jaws,
And brown fur mittens on my big brown paws.
With a big brown furry-down up to my head,
I'd sleep all winter in a big fur bed.

All But Blind

WALTER DE LA MARE

All but blind
    In his chambered hole
Gropes for worms
    The four-clawed Mole.

All but blind
    In the evening sky
The hooded Bat
    Twirls softly by.

All but blind
    In the burning day
The Barn-Owl blunders
    On her way.

And blind as are
    These three to me,
So, blind to Some-One
    I must be.

'Poor Bird'

WALTER DE LA MARE

Poor bird! –
No hands, no fingers thine;
Two angle-coloured wings instead:
But where are mine?

Cold voiceless fish! –
No hands, no spindly legs, no toes;
But fins and a tail,
And a mouth for nose.

Wild Weed! –
Not even an eye with which to see!
Or ear or tongue,
For sigh or song;
Or heart to beat,
Or mind to long.

And yet – ah, would that I,
In sun and shade, like thee,
Might no less gentle, sweet,
And lovely be!

Glory and Eternity

G

Pied Beauty

GERARD MANLEY HOPKINS

Glory be to God for dappled things –
    For skies of couple-colour as a brinded cow;
       For rose-moles all in stipple upon trout that swim;
Fresh-firecoal chestnut-falls; finches' wings . . .

The Golden Cat

ELEANOR FARJEON

My golden cat has dappled sides;
No prince has worn so fine a cloak
Patterned like sea-water where rides
The sun, or like the flower in oak
When the rough plank has been planed out,
Lovely as yellow mackerel skies
In moonlight, or a speckled trout.
Clear as swung honey were his eyes.

It was a wondrous daily thing
To look for, when his beautiful
Curved body gathered for a spring
That, light as any golden gull,
Flashed over the fine net of wire
Which my casement-window bars;
His leap was bright as tongues of fire,
And swift as autumn shooting-stars.

My cat was like a golden gift,
A golden myth of Grecian lore –
But things so bright, and things so swift,
Must vanish; and he is no more.

A Living

D. H. LAWRENCE

A bird
picks up its seeds or little snails
between heedless earth and heaven
in heedlessness.

But, the plucky little sport, it gives to life
song, and chirruping, gay feathers, fluff-shadowe
    warmth
and all the unspeakable charm of birds hopping an
    fluttering and being birds,
– And we, we get it all from them for nothing.

The Wild Swans at Coole

The trees are in their autumn beauty,
The woodland paths are dry,
Under the October twilight the water
Mirrors a still sky;
Upon the brimming water among the stones
Are nine-and-fifty swans.

The nineteenth Autumn has come upon me
Since I first made my count;
I saw, before I had well finished,
All suddenly mount
And scatter wheeling in great broken rings
Upon their clamorous wings.

I have looked upon those brilliant creatures,
And now my heart is sore.
All's changed since I, hearing at twilight,
The first time on this shore,
The bell-beat of their wings above my head,
Trod with a lighter tread.

Unwearied still, lover by lover,
They paddle in the cold
Companionable streams or climb the air;

Their hearts have not grown old;
Passion or conquest, wander where they will,
Attend upon them still.

But now they drift on the still water,
Mysterious, beautiful;
Among what rushes will they build,
By what lake's edge or pool
Delight men's eyes when I awake some day
To find they have flown away?

To a Cat

A. C. SWINBURNE

Stately, kindly, lordly friend,
     Condescend
Here to sit by me, and turn
Glorious eyes, love's lustrous meed,
On the golden page I read.

All your wondrous wealth of hair,
     Dark and fair,
Silken-shaggy, soft and bright
As the clouds and beams of night,
Pays my reverent hand's caress
Back with friendlier gentleness.

Dogs may fawn on all and some
     As they come;
You, a friend of loftier mind,
Answer friends alone in kind.
Just your foot upon my hand
Softly bids it understand.

Self-Pity

D. H. LAWRENCE

I never saw a wild thing
sorry for itself.
A small bird will drop frozen dead from a bough
without ever having felt sorry for itself.

Vespers

T. E. BROWN

O blackbird, what a boy you are!
How you do go it!
Blowing your bugle to that one sweet star –
How you do blow it!
And does she hear you, blackbird boy, so far?
Or is it wasted breath?
'Good Lord! She is so bright
Tonight!'
The blackbird saith.

The Throstle

ALFRED LORD TENNYSON

'Summer is coming, summer is coming,
    I know it, I know it, I know it.
Light again, leaf again, life again, love again,'
    Yes, my wild little Poet.

Sing the new year in under the blue.
    Last year you sang it as gladly.
'New, new, new, new!' Is it then *so* new
    That you should carol so madly?

'Love again, song again, nest again, young again,'
    Never a prophet so crazy!
And hardly a daisy as yet, little friend,
    See, there is hardly a daisy.

'Here again, here, here, here, happy year!'
    O warble unchidden, unbidden!
Summer is coming, is coming, my dear,
    And all the winters are hidden.

The Lily-Pool

T. E. BROWN

What sees our mailie* in the lily-pool,
    What sees she with that large surprise?
What sees our mailie in the lily-pool
    With all the violet of her big eyes –
        Our mailie in the lily-pool?

She sees herself within the lily-pool
    Herself in flakes of brown and white –
Herself beneath the slab that is the lily-pool,
    The green and liquid slab of light
    With cups of silver dight,
    Stem-rooted in the depths of amber night
That hold the hollows of the lily-pool –
    Our own dear lily-pool!

And does she gaze into the lily-pool
    As one that is enchanted?
Or does she try the cause to find
    How the reflection's slanted,
That sleeps within the lily-pool?
    Or does she take it all for granted,
With the sweet natural logic of her kind?
        The lazy logic of the lily-pool,
        Our own bright, innocent, stupid lily-pool!

* A mailie is a cow without horns.

203

She knows that it is nice – our lily-pool:
　　She likes the water-rings around her knees;
　　She likes the shadow of the trees,
That droop above the lily-pool;
　　She likes to scatter with a silly sneeze
The long-legged flies that skim the lily-pool –
The peaceful-sleeping, baby lily-pool.

So may I look upon the lily-pool,
　　Nor ever in the slightest care
　　Why I am there;
Why upon land and sea
Is ever stamped the inevitable me;
But rather say with that most gentle fool: –
'How pleasant is this lily-pool!
How nice and cool!
Be off, you long-legged flies! O what a spree!
To drive the flies from off the lily-pool!
From off this most sufficient, absolute lily-pool!'

Many Mansions

D. H. LAWRENCE

When a bird flips his tail in getting his balance on a tree
he feels much gayer than if somebody had left him a for-
    tune
or than if he'd just built himself a nest with a bathroom –
Why can't people be gay like that?

Song's Eternity

JOHN CLARE

What is song's eternity?
Come and see.
Can it noise and bustle be?
Come and see.
Praises sung or praises said
Can it be?
Wait awhile and these are dead –
Sigh, sigh;
Be they high or lowly bred
They die.

What is song's eternity?
Come and see.
Melodies of earth and sky,
Here they be.
Song once sung to Adam's ears
Can it be?
Ballads of six thousand years
Thrive, thrive;
Song awakens with the spheres
Alive.

Mighty songs that miss decay,
What are they?
Crowds and cities pass away
Like a day.

Books are out and books are read;
What are they?
Years will lay them with the dead –
Sigh, sigh;
Trifles unto nothing wed,
They die.

Dreamers, mark the honey bee;
Mark the tree
Where the blue cap '*tootle tee*'
Sings a glee
Sung to Adam and to Eve –
Here they be.
When floods covered every bough,
Noah's ark
Heard that ballad singing now;
Hark, hark,

'*Tootle tootle tootle tee*' –
Can it be
Pride and fame must shadows be?
Come and see –
Every season owns her own;
Bird and bee
Sing creation's music on;
Nature's glee
Is in every mood and tone
Eternity.

Nightingale

JOHN KEATS

Thou wast not born for death, immortal Bird!
  No hungry generations tread thee down;
The voice I hear this passing night was heard
  In ancient days by emperor and clown:
Perhaps the selfsame song that found a path
  Through the sad heart of Ruth, when, sick for home,
    She stood in tears amid the alien corn;
      The same that oft-times hath
Charm'd magic casements, opening on the foam
  Of perilous seas, in faery lands forlorn.

(from *Ode to a Nightingale*)

Similar Cases

CHARLOTTE PERKINS GILMAN

There was once a little animal
    No bigger than a fox,
And on five toes he scampered
    Over Tertiary rocks.
They called him Eohippus,
    And they called him very small,
And they thought him of no value
    (When they thought of him at all);
For the lumpish Dinoceras
    And Coryphodont so slow
Were the heavy aristocracy
    In days of long ago.

Said the little Eohippus:
    'I am going to be a horse,
And on my middle finger-nails
    To run my earthly course;
I'm going to have a flowing tail,
    I'm going to have a mane,
I'm going to stand fourteen hands high
    On the psychozoic plain.'
The Coryphodont was horrified,
    The Dinoceras shocked;
And they chased young Eohippus,
    But he skipped away and mocked.

Then they laughed enormous laughter,
    And they groaned enormous groans,
And they bade young Eohippus
    Go and view his father's bones.
Said they: 'You always were as small
    And mean as now we see,
And therefore it is evident
    That you're always going to be.'
'What! Be a great, tall, handsome beast
    With hoofs to gallop on?
Why, you'd have to change your nature!'
    Said the Loxolophodon.

They considered him disposed of,
    And retired with gait serene,
That was the way they argued
    In the early Eocene.

Lady Zouch

ELEANOR FARJEON

Lady Zouch could not keep deer
    Today in Parham Park
If Noah had not long ago
    Kept deer inside the Ark.
I hope that Lady Zouch today
    Thanks Noah long ago
For every spotted fawn that runs
    With every dappled doe.

Index of Poets' Names

Index of First Lines

216

*Some more anthologies
of poetry in Puffins are described
on the following pages*

A PUFFIN BOOK OF VERSE

Compiled by Eleanor Graham

PS 72

This anthology is intended simply to give pleasure, and it is hoped that every boy or girl who browses among its pages will find something to enjoy.

It ranges from nursery rhymes and nonsense poems to verses whose meaning has to be thought about: but whether the poems are simple or more difficult, they have been chosen partly for that beauty of rhythm and language which makes lines linger in the mind after the book that contains them has been put aside.

A PUFFIN QUARTET OF POETS

Edited by Eleanor Graham

PS 121

This unusual anthology contains a selection of poems from the work of only four poets, but four of the finest who are writing verse for children to-day. A substantial amount from the work of each is given, enough to show their individual quality and special characteristics. The quartet is made up of Eleanor Farjeon, James Reeves, E. V. Rieu, and Ian Serraillier. There are brief biographical notes and a short introduction to each section suggesting how these poets go to work. Their methods of approach to verse-making proved, in fact, to be so diverse that together they cast much interesting light on the whole subject of composition.

A CHILD'S GARDEN OF VERSES

Robert Louis Stevenson

PS 22

There are more than sixty famous verses by Robert Louis Stevenson in this book, and they are illustrated with many drawings by Eve Garnett. 'These are rhymes, jingles,' the author wrote to a friend, 'I don't go in for eternity and the three unities.' They are rhymes about his childhood, divided into three sections – *The Child Alone, Garden Days,* and *Envoys.*